BANG BANG YOU'RE DEAD

by Louise Fitzhugh and Sandra Scoppettone

Pictures by Louise Fitzhugh

Harper & Row, Publishers • New York, Evanston, and London

For my mother

Louise Fitzhugh

For my mother and father

Sandra Scoppettone

Bang, bang, you're dead," said James.
"I'm a big, brave, strong soldier and soldiers always win."

He marched out and met his friends Timothy, Stanley, and Bert.
"All right, men," said James. "Let's play Bang, Bang, You're Dead."

At the bottom of the hill James said, "Today Stanley and me are the good guys, and Timothy and Bert are the bad guys."

"That's not fair," said Timothy. "I was a bad guy yesterday."

"Okay," said James. "You be a good guy today.

First army to take the hill wins," yelled James.
They all ran for cover.

Bert and Stanley looked out and couldn't see anyone.
They started up the hill.

Timothy and James looked out and couldn't see anyone.
They started up the hill.

Then, at the top of the hill—

they all shot at once. "Bang, bang, you're dead," yelled Stanley.
"*Ooph, arragh, omphph,*" said Timothy, dying, as he shot Stanley.
"Bang, bang, you're — *oomahrphm,*" said James, "you got me."
"I got you dead," said Bert. "Bang!"
"I got you dead back," yelled James.

They all lay dead.

They all got up and marched down the hill—

and celebrated the end of the war.

One day ...

as James and Timothy and Stanley and Bert were playing war, a strange thing happened.

"Who are you?" shouted James. "This is our hill."

"I'm Big Mike and it's our hill now," said the tallest one.

"We had it first," said Bert.

"Tough," said the big one. "You'll have to take it away from us."

"We will," said James.

"Okay," said Big Mike, "three o'clock tomorrow."

James and his army went to headquarters, the tree house.
"This is real war," said James. "I'll get that Big Mike.
Where does he get off saying it's his hill?"
"Yeah, we'll fix those skunks. Let's chop off their heads!"
"Let's get big rocks and smash them!"
"Let's make a pact. We'll fight

to the end!"

It was three o'clock on the day of The Great War.
The two armies met at the bottom of the hill.

"Give up, puke-face. You don't have a chance," said Big Mike.
"Up your nose, you freak-out," yelled James. "Okay, men, take cover."
 The war began.

U.S. 1923754

25

There were screams, yells, blood, and pain.

It was awful.

There was a terrible moaning and groaning.
James looked around.
No one was fighting. They all lay hurting.
"This isn't any fun," said Timothy. "Why did we do it?"

No one could answer.
"Nobody won," said James.
"We all lost," said the smallest one to his tooth.
"Well, who gets the hill?"

James and Big Mike looked at each other.
"Why don't we just use it..." said James.
"...together?" said Big Mike.

"Then there'd be more people to play with."
"Let's all come back tomorrow."
"And play war?"
"Real war?"

"No, you know," said James, "Bang, Bang, You're Dead."